SASHA visits BANG

Illu...
W... ... by Shamini Flint

Book Four: Sasha in Asia

Sasha is visiting Bangkok with her Mamma. Bangkok is the capital of Thailand.

Sasha is given a garland of beautiful purple orchids at the airport.

It is a welcome present.

Sasha soon learns how to greet people in traditional Thai style!

Sasha and Mamma decide to go sightseeing.

Sasha sees many small, three-wheeled vehicles.

"What are those, Mamma?"

"They are special Bangkok taxis known as
tuk tuks, Sasha."

Can you guess why they are called *tuk tuks*?

It is because the engines make a '*tuk tuk*'
sound!

Sasha and Mamma pass some young boys on the road.

They are wearing bright saffron robes and their heads are shaved.

"Mamma, who are they?"

"They are boy monks, Sasha. They live and study in the temples around Bangkok."

Sasha and Mamma walk towards the Grand Palace.

Sasha is transfixed by the exotic buildings and the golden *stupa*.

A dome-shaped structure is called a *stupa* in Thailand.

"Does the King of Thailand live here, Mamma?"

"No, Sasha. Not anymore. But the King still visits the palace sometimes."

Sasha and Mamma visit the Temple
of the Emerald Buddha.

"Mamma, look at that! What is it?"

"It is the statue of a mythical guardian
that protects the temple, Sasha."

Can you see the orange and green tiles
on the gleaming temple roofs?

The next morning, Sasha and Mamma head
towards the *khlong* – the canals in Bangkok.

There are small wooden boats laden
with fruit and vegetables on the water.

The women are wearing flat-topped,
conical straw hats.

"Look, Sasha! It is a floating market."

Sasha has never been shopping on
a boat before!

Later that day, Mamma and Sasha watch a traditional Thai dance.

The dancers are very graceful.

They are dressed in beautiful silk costumes and wear elaborate headgear.

Sasha tries to copy the dancing.

She whispers, "Look at me, Mamma. I am dancing too!"

Sasha takes part in an elephant parade!

Elephants in Thailand are often used as transport and to carry heavy loads.

The elephants are walking slowly and majestically down the street.

Sasha is excited and a little bit nervous.

She holds on tight. She does not want to fall off!

The next day is Songkran, the Thai New Year.

Many people are visiting their families and going to the temple.

The Thai people also celebrate the New Year by splashing water on each other for luck.

They use cups, bowls and water pistols.

Sasha joins in. It is such fun.

"Mamma, I'm all wet!"

Sasha and Mamma stop at the Chatuchak weekend market.

There are hundreds of stalls selling everything from statues to silk.

Sasha and Mamma wander around looking for presents to take back home.

Sasha especially likes the puppets. Mamma buys her one as a souvenir.

"Mamma, I've had a lovely time in Bangkok!"

The "Sasha in Asia" Books

SASHA visits BALI
Illustrated by Alpana Ahuja
Written by Shamini Flint
Book One: Sasha in Asia

SASHA visits KUALA LUMPUR
Illustrated by Alpana Ahuja
Written by Shamini Flint
Book Two: Sasha in Asia

SASHA visits HONG KONG
Illustrated by Alpana Ahuja
Written by Shamini Flint
Book Three: Sasha in Asia

SASHA visits BANGKOK
Illustrated by Alpana Ahuja
Written by Shamini Flint
Book Four: Sasha in Asia

The "Sasha in Singapore" Books